The Charlotte Harbor N~
is pleased to give th

MW00638999

We hope you enjoy reading about our natural environment.

Adventures in the Charlotte Harbor Watershed
A Story of Four Animals and Their Neighborhoods
Edited by Maran Brainard Hilgendorf, CHNEP
Written by Carol Mahler
Illustrated by Rachel Rebekah Renne
Designed by Angela VanEmmerik (2008) and Maran Hilgendorf (2014)

Learn about the environment of southwest Florida through the adventures of four animals:
- a yellow-crowned night-heron on the Caloosahatchee River
- an alligator in the Peace River
- an otter on the Myakka River
- a mullet in the estuaries

The Charlotte Harbor National Estuary Program is a partnership to protect the natural environment of southwest Florida. The CHNEP developed this book to help children better understand the natural environment of southwest Florida.

The CHNEP and its partners are pleased to provide other resources to help make all who live, work and play in the region better stewards of the precious natural resources found here. Please visit *www.CHNEP.org* for information on grants, resources for children, a guide of special places to learn about the environment (parks, nature centers, etc.), special events and much more.

Dedication
This edition of *Adventures* is dedicated to Pam Burt. Pam was a dedicated educator, compassionate and caring friend, and a life-long learner and protector of the environment. Her memory will live on through the pages of this book.

Acknowledgements

The Charlotte Harbor National Estuary Program is a partnership working to protect the natural environment in Florida from Venice to Bonita Springs to Winter Haven.

Special thanks to the author, illustrator and designer who generously provided their talents to this book, to the CHNEP Citizens Advisory Committee (CAC) for their support, to Janice Sylvain, Rachelle Selser, Stacia Hetrick, Lisa Beever, Rae Ann Wessel, Greg Blanchard, Theresa Schober, Natalie Balcer, Forest Reynolds and Kaley Miller for their careful reviews of the book and to the school districts for their cooperation and support.

Because of its financial partners and the generous support of sponsors, the CHNEP is able to distribute the book free to students throughout the seven counties that participate in the Program.

The CHNEP financial partners are the U.S. Environmental Protection Agency, Southwest Florida Water Management District, South Florida Water Management District, Florida Department of Environmental Protection, Florida Coastal Zone Management Program, Peace River Manasota Regional Water Supply Authority, the counties of Charlotte, DeSoto, Hardee, Lee, Manatee, Polk and Sarasota, and the cities and towns of Bonita Springs, Cape Coral, Fort Myers, Fort Myers Beach, North Port, Punta Gorda, Sanibel, Venice and Winter Haven.

Florida Wildlife Federation

Keeping the Wild in Florida since 1936!

The Jelks Family Foundation supported the second and sixth editions (2009 and 2013). An anonymous donor supported the fourth edition (2011) in memory of Virgil I. Pitstick. The Hildred Schloss Revocable Trust supported the fifth edition (2012). Florida Wildlife Federation supported the seventh and eighth editions (2014 and 2014–2015).
— **Maran Brainard Hilgendorf, Editor**

The author thanks Maran Brainard Hilgendorf and the Charlotte Harbor National Estuary Program for their patience, encouragement and support of this project; the environmental educators and scientists who shared their time, expertise and words: Desiree A. Companion, Barbara Davis, Lisa Figueroa, Anita Forester, Bill Hammond, Diane Herron, Kayton Nedza, Melissa Cain Nell, Dr. Charles O'Connor, Curtis Porterfield, Tina Powell, and Rachel Rebekah Renne for these beautiful drawings. She also thanks her daughter, Jahna Peace Leonard, for her company as they explored the estuary in the car and on foot; her husband for piloting her through the estuary by truck, boat and airplane; and Stanley Forester, Luke Wilson and Elise Zarli for their critique.

The author acknowledges a debt of inspiration to Holling Clancy Holling for his books *Minn of the Mississippi, Pagoo, Paddle-to-the-Sea* and *Seabird*. — **Carol Mahler, Author**

The artist thanks the sun, clouds, trees, water, soil, birds, mammals, reptiles, fish, amphibians and invertebrates, especially the insects, for their naturally artful existence, and she thanks the children for whom this book is drawn. — **Rachel Rebekah Renne, Illustrator**

Contents

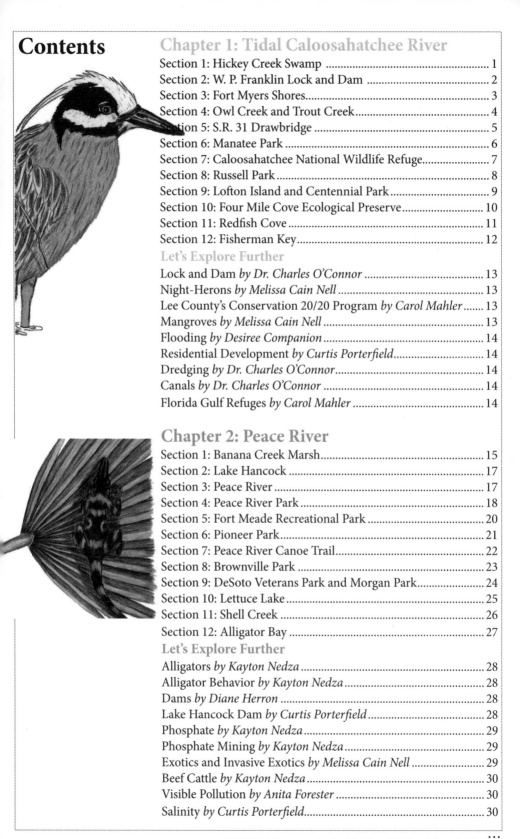

Chapter 1: Tidal Caloosahatchee River

Chapter 2: Peace River

Contents
(continued)

Chapter 3: Myakka River

Chapter 4: Estuaries
from Dona and Roberts Bays to Estero Bay

Chapter 1
Tidal Caloosahatchee River

Section 1: Hickey Creek Swamp

Near the Caloosahatchee River, a male yellow-crowned night-heron builds a nest. He weaves together sticks and twigs. Inside, he places grass and leaves make it soft. The nest is hidden in the branches of a cypress tree.

The male greets the female bird. As part of mating, they bow, raise the feathers on their necks and call softly to each other. They also fly in circles. After a short time, the female lays three pale blue eggs in the nest, sits on them for three weeks, and they hatch.

Mother and father both work to feed the babies. First they find crabs to eat. Then, they fly back to the nest. They bring the food they have swallowed back up from their stomachs and feed it to their babies. When the babies are three or four weeks old, they learn to fly and to catch their own meals.

A northwest wind pushes cold weather, and the wind blows one young heron away from his family.

Section 2: W. P Franklin Lock and Dam

Gray clouds fan across the sky like the spread wing of a bird, and the young heron sits on a fence post. Often, gulls and anhingas perch on the walls and railings of the lock and dam.

The lock must be opened to allow boats to travel to and from Lake Okeechobee. No boats are here now. The heron is alone.

Rain spatters the metal walkway. Quick steps sound an echo on the bridge from the shore. A man runs toward the heron.

When he sees the heron, the man stops. Breathing deeply, he scans up and down the river. Then he quietly turns to the heron. "Well, little fellow, looks like we're the only ones to brave this weather."

The heron ruffles its feathers.

"You're not hurt, are you?" the man asks.

The man tilts his head, looking closely. "Doesn't look like it. You're a yellow-crowned night-heron, aren't you? Scientists call you *Nyctanassa violacea*. That's a noisy name for a shy bird. How about I call you Nick?"

The wind gusts, and the man looks at the sky. "It may not be night, but it's dark. Is this your kind of weather?" the man asks.

The heron turns its head toward the wind.

"Looks like it's going to get worse." The man zips his coat.

The noise startles Nick, and he spreads his wings. In the air, the wind seems to toss him away.

"Goodbye, Nick!" the man calls, but his voice is lost in the wind.

Section 3: Fort Myers Shores

Behind a house in Fort Myers Shores is a dock. An older woman and a boy walk to the end. Under them, Nick stands in the water.

"Grandma, the river doesn't seem to be moving," the boy says.

"That's because the river mostly flows in the deep channel in the middle. This is an oxbow of the river," the woman says.

The boy leans on the railing. Nick watches his reflection in the water. "What's an oxbow?"

"It's two things, really." She moves her hands to show the shape. "It's a U-shaped piece of wood that fits around the neck of an ox. When a river turns to make that same U-shape and is cut off from the main flow of the river, it's called an oxbow. This is a shallow oxbow that was bypassed when the channel was dug and the river became the Okeechobee Waterway, or C-43 Canal. It links the Gulf of Mexico and the Atlantic Ocean," the woman says.

The boy picks up a beetle and places it on the railing. "How do you take the curves out of a river?"

The woman sighs. "It wasn't easy. It takes a big machine called a dredge. It's like a bulldozer, and it digs sand out of the river."

"Wow! I want to see that!" the boy says.

Nick walks closer to a piling beneath the dock.

"It was a long time ago. Workers began to dig canals to connect the Gulf of Mexico and the Atlantic Ocean and to drain marshes and wetlands to make drier land for houses and farming. They had to dynamite a waterfall to do it."

"You mean the river didn't flow from Lake Okeechobee?" the boy asks. He flicks the beetle off the railing, and Nick watches it plop on the water.

"It did, but not like today. It was very shallow — like they say of the Everglades — a river of grass," the woman says.

The boy watches the beetle. Nick does too.

The woman says, "The riverbed used to be white sand, and now it's covered with silt from the lake. The channel's been widened and deepened several times. It's perfect for boats."

Nick leans out from under the dock to catch the beetle.

The boy points. "That bird just ate my bug!"

Nick flies away.

Section 4: Owl Creek and Trout Creek

Owl Creek and Trout Creek flow into the river, not far from the Lee Civic Center. Nick stands in the shallow water and, through the reeds, sees two fishermen on the shore.

"Did you hear that RiverWatch got an oxbow restored up by old Fort Denaud?" The first man jerks the rod as he reels.

The second man baits his hook, and Nick watches the minnow in his hands.

"What do you mean — restored?" The second man casts his line. Nick watches the bait fly through the air and splash into the water.

"They did some digging so the water would flow. They planted a bunch of plants to keep the water clean, even though it moves slowly. There's even an oxbow island." The first man pulls up his hook and checks the bait. Nick watches him cast.

The second man feels a tug on his line. He yanks his fishing rod to set the hook, but his line is loose. Nick sees a blue crab stealing the bait.

The second man says, "It can't be the way it used to be. I remember my grandfather's stories. Somewhere the river used to make a curve like an S. Steamboats couldn't steer around it."

The first man asks, "So they turned around and went back to Fort Myers?"

Nick grabs the crab and eats it.

"Nope. The boatmen tied ropes to the trees. They pulled the boats around the curves. It was called 'Rope Bend.' It was famous, and they even made it into picture postcards." The second man pulls up an empty hook.

Nick walks away from the voices.

Section 5: S.R. 31 Drawbridge

S.R. 31, known by some as Dixie Highway, crosses the river east of Fort Myers. Nick stands on a piling. Above him is a small house on the side of the bridge. Inside, the bridge tender makes sure that cars and trucks stop so the drawbridge can open for boats.

Just east of the bridge, a sailboat sounds its horn. It is too tall to pass under and waits for the bridge to open.

The bridge tender turns on the alarm bells. The noise is loud, but Nick doesn't fly away. Red lights flash on the gates. When lowered, the gates keep cars and trucks off the bridge.

When the bridge is empty of cars and trucks, the tender turns on the motors and Nick feels the throbbing. At the center of the bridge span, two sections of the bridge rise.

After the boat passes through, the bridge sections lower into place. Joined again at the center, the bridge is now safe for cars and trucks to pass. The gates are raised, the lights stop flashing and the bells stop ringing. Nick hears the hum of tires as traffic moves across the bridge again.

He also hears the cry of gulls and sees them behind the boat as they swoop and dive in the wake. They are catching small fish that tumble to the surface as the boat's propeller churns the water.

From the piling, Nick flies to the shallow water near shore where some of the small fish scatter. He catches and eats one, and then another.

Section 6: Manatee Park

On the south bank of the river looms the Florida Power and Light plant. Built in 1958, it used to burn diesel fuel to make electricity. Since 2002, it burns natural gas. Water for cooling the plant's hot engines comes from the river. The heated water flows into a canal that drains into Orange River.

On the west side of the canal and along the north shore of the river is Orange River Preserve, purchased by Lee County's Conservation 20/20 Program. A bird watcher there sees Nick fly above the canal. On the east side of the canal is Manatee Park. The land is owned by the power company. Lee County and other groups pay for the building and the people who work there. Many volunteers also help.

Nick lands on the bank of the canal and hears a guide say, "I see a group of manatees just at the entrance. They come here when the temperature in the Gulf falls below 68 degrees." She shades her eyes with one hand and points with the other.

"Here's one," a girl says. She stands with her mother and brother on the sidewalk behind a fence that surrounds the manatee viewing area.

"Look at its snout. It's ugly." A boy kicks at the ground with one foot.

Their mother says, "You're seeing it through the water, so it looks strange, like when you see your friend underwater in the swimming pool."

"Is it looking for something to eat?" the girl asks.

The guide says, "Manatees aren't fish, so they have to surface to breathe. They need air to live, just like we do."

"What do they eat?" the girl asks.

"They eat seagrasses and other plants that grow in the water. That's why they're called sea cows," the guide says.

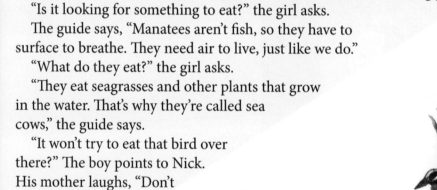

"It won't try to eat that bird over there?" The boy points to Nick. His mother laughs, "Don't be silly. You've never seen a cow try to eat a bird."

"I'd like to, though." The boy kicks the fence, and it rattles.

Nick flies away.

Section 7: Caloosahatchee National Wildlife Refuge

On Interstate 75, cars and trucks roar across the bridges. On the river's north shore, the interstate cuts through the Caloosahatchee Creeks Preserve. The mangrove islands nearby form the Caloosahatchee National Wildlife Refuge.

Nick stands in the water near the mangroves. A lizard runs along a branch. A breeze rustles the cabbage palms and sea grapes that grow at the island's center.

Two white egrets and a great blue heron hunt for fish. In the water, three pelicans have eaten and are resting.

The breeze blows again. Nick watches a mangrove leaf fall. Beneath it, he sees many leaves sunk into the water. They are caught in the prop roots of the mangrove. As the water moves, they are ground into smaller and smaller pieces. Animals too small to see live on and eat these bits. Tiny shrimp and baby fish feed on them.

A Styrofoam cup bobs between the roots. A bead of Styrofoam breaks free. It mixes with the leaf bits. If something eats the bead, it could get sick.

A fiddler crab runs across the sand. Nick stabs for it but misses. He stalks across the sand. His footprints join those of crabs, ibis and gulls.

Section 8: Russell Park

Railroad bridges, called trestles, cross the water between small islands. At sunset, Nick flies over. His shadow slides along the tracks like a train.

Boats usually travel in the middle of the river where the water is deepest. The track that crosses the channel is raised like a drawbridge so boats can pass under. Nick lands on the top and looks at the houses and docks built on the shores.

He flies to the south shore and lands near the Russell Park Boat Launch. A driveway of gravel slopes into the river. The grass on either side of the driveway is blocked off with "no parking" signs.

Nick stands very still when he sees a frog hopping across the grass.

Across the street are many historic homes. In front of one, a woman and a girl walk out and down the front porch steps. They hold hands as they walk to the street and stop. The woman points at Nick. "See the bird?"

"What kind is it, Mommy?" the girl asks.

The frog hops closer to Nick and eats a mosquito.

"Some kind of heron, I think. Look at its long legs," the woman says.

The girl rubs her leg. "Bugs are biting me, but I can't see them!"

"They are tiny flies called no-see-ums." The woman slaps her arm. "The mosquitoes are biting too. Let's go back in."

"Will the bird go home?" the girl asks.

"I think it's a kind of night heron. Like an owl, it hunts at night."

As they walk away, the girl waves her hand. "Bye, bye, birdie."

The frog leaps very close to Nick, and he grabs it in his bill.

Section 9: Lofton Island and Centennial Park

Nick flies over the bridges, which are the north and south lanes of U.S. Highway Business 41. They were built high above the river, so even tall boats can pass under. Nick lands in the water beside an island.

Two men sit in the shade of Australian pines. When the breeze blows the branches, the sound is like waves washing the shore. The first man asks, "Did you know this island was named for a fellow named Lofton?"

The second man pours coffee from a thermos into a cup. "Who's he?"

The first man says, "He dredged the river back in 1910. He made it wider and deeper from here to LaBelle. This island is sand he dug from near the south shore where the Fort Myers Yacht Basin is now."

Nick watches dragonflies zip over the water.

The second man sips his coffee. "This is a huge pile of sand. The river must have been very shallow."

Standing very still, Nick sees a mud crab.

The first man says, "It was different then. Docks with packing houses jutted out into deep water. Two piers even had tracks for trains!"

"So what happened?" the second man asks.

"The docks were taken out because most businesses had failed. It was the Great Depression. Sand dredged from the yacht basin filled in the waterfront to make Centennial Park."

A fish crow lands on the branches above Nick.

The first man looks at it. "Are you an American crow?"

The crow tilts its head, ruffles its feathers and says, "Uhn-uhn."

"I knew it!" the first man slaps his leg. "That's a fish crow. I see them over at the park. They're always at the fishing pier and near the boat ramp."

The second man points at Nick.

"I see herons like that one when I'm at the park."

As the men walk away, Nick grabs the crab. The fish crow dives at Nick. It wants to steal the crab, but Nick eats it. The fish crow flies away.

Section 10: Four Mile Cove Ecological Preserve

In the late afternoon, Nick soars over the Caloosahatchee Bridge where Tamiami Trail crosses the river. On the south shore are large estates. In the late nineteenth century, Thomas Edison, Henry Ford and Harvey Firestone built beautiful houses, and other people have too. Seawalls line the river.

When Nick reaches the Midpoint Bridge, he flies to the north shore. It's called Four Mile Point. The Cape Coral Parks and Recreation Department manages this land as Four Mile Cove Ecological Preserve.

Nick lands in a black mangrove, and crabs scuttle away from him.

Two women are walking along the boardwalk. One is pushing a stroller. In the stroller, a little boy is eating a rice cake and dropping crumbs.

The first woman says, "The trail guide says that lightning killed this area of mangroves."

The second woman says, "I wondered why they were dead. Look how much sun comes through."

A rice cake crumb drops. Nick watches a crab find and eat it.

"It says here that the soil is so wet that the lightning charge spread out."

The woman reading the trail guide stops and looks at the muck.

Nick flutters beside the pneumatophores — a specialized root — and the crab zips away.

The woman with the trail guide says, "I can see the small holes that are burrows for the fiddler crabs."

The second woman looks back over her shoulder. "C'mon, it's getting late. I want to see the cove. The canoe trail has picnic shelters built out in the water."

The woman with the trail guide hurry to catch up. A breeze pushes more rice cake crumbs into the water.

When a crab nibbles a crumb, Nick snatches the crab and eats it.

Section 11: Redfish Cove

At dawn, Nick flies over the Cape Coral Bridge. He passes the boat ramp at Peppertree Pointe and flies into the shadows beneath the fishing pier. He hears people walking and sees lines from fishing poles in the water.

A boy pulls up a fish on his hook. Nick hears people crowding around. The boy says, "Hey, Mom. What kind of fish is this?"

"I don't know, but it's beautiful," his mom says.

The boy persists, "I want to know what kind of fish it is."

The fish wiggles, and drops of water from the fish fall near Nick.

A man says, "That's a redfish. This stretch of water is full of them. It's called Redfish Cove."

The woman asks, "Is it good to eat?"

The man nods his head. "Yes, ma'am, but it's not big enough to keep."

The woman says, "Such a beautiful fish. Throw it back, son."

The boy slips the fish from the hook. He strokes its body as if he were petting a dog.

The man says, "You shouldn't rub a fish like that. It can hurt a special film on the skin that protects the fish from getting sick."

The boy flings the fish over the railing. "Bye, bye, fish!"

Nick watches the fish hit the water, but it is too big for him to eat. He flies to the roof of the shelter at the end of the pier. Looking toward the shore, he sees a restaurant, the Yacht Club Community Park beach and a playground. Children sound as loud as gulls as they play.

On either side of the beach are seawalls. They contain the lawns of houses and form the banks of Cape Coral's canals. Nick turns to the river. Large and small boats zoom inside the channel. Across the water, he sees big houses and buildings. The river seems as wide as a lake or bay.

When Nick hears footsteps walking toward him, he flies away.

Section 12: Fisherman Key

At the west end of Redfish Cove, land juts into the river. Tall pines gave it the name Piney Point. Nick lands there and looks across the river.

The south shore also curves into the river. At the west end of Iona Cove is Shell Point, where a parking lot surrounds tall buildings. Between Piney Point and Shell Point, the river is narrow. In the dusk, Nick watches boats with red, green and white lights in the channel.

Nick flies along the north shore, between Piney Point and Sword Point. Moonlight sparkles on the water and reflects on the shiny mangrove leaves.

Turning south, Nick flies over the mouth of the river. Where it flows into San Carlos Bay, a delta is formed. Many oysters grow here, one on top of another. The huge mound is called an oyster reef, or shoal. At low tide, it looks like an island. More than 100 years ago, this oyster shoal blocked the way for boats to go upstream. Part of it was destroyed when a channel was dug.

The south edge of the delta is Punta Rassa, which used to be a busy port for shipping cows in the nineteenth century. Today, Punta Rassa is where the Sanibel Causeway begins. Nick veers away from the headlights of traffic.

As he flies toward Fisherman Key, he squawks. He hears another bird make the same call. He watches another yellow-crowned night-heron land on a tidal flat to the east of the key. Moonlight gleams on the wet sand. There are others like him feeding there and even some black-crowned night-herons.

Maybe Nick has found a home.

Let's Explore Further

Lock and Dam *by Dr. Charles O'Connor*

The man-made lock and dam on the Caloosahatchee block the water from its natural gravity flow toward the west, creating a pool behind the structure. The lock is the "gate" that boats and manatees pass through to get to the other side. The dam features a series of lift gates where water can be passed through the concrete wall. The dam is used to release water from the upstream side when water levels get too high.

In 1965, Franklin Lock and Dam were built to prevent salt water from moving further upriver. This protects fresh water that is used for drinking and for crops. There are two other locks and dams on the Caloosahatchee River and all three have changed the river. The river used to be a curvy, shallow river that was an estuary. But the dams have helped create two long, narrow freshwater lakes. The water doesn't flow as much and silt (mud) is a big problem.

Night-Herons *by Melissa Cain Nell*

Florida has two kinds of night herons: black-crowned and yellow-crowned. As chicks, both have golden eyes and brown-and-white-streaked feathers. Adult black-crowned have red eyes and gray feathers. The yellow-crowned head is black with a white stripe on its cheek. Named for their bright yellow forehead, both males and females grow a long, white feathery "crown" when looking for a mate. They are called "night" birds, but they often feed in the evening and morning. They eat blue crabs, mud crabs, mangrove crabs, fiddler crabs, small fish, aquatic insects, and even frogs.

Lee County's Conservation 20/20 Program *by Carol Mahler*

In 1995, some citizens wanted to preserve natural areas in Lee County. They asked the government to help and, in 1996, voters agreed to pay more taxes to buy wild lands. Similar land acquisition programs exist in Charlotte, Polk and Sarasota counties.

Mangroves *by Melissa Cain Nell*

Mangroves are trees that can live near salt water. They protect the coasts and build new land by keeping sand from washing away and by breaking the force of strong waves caused by storms. Mangrove roots offer hiding places for young fish and shellfish. Their branches are homes for different birds. A rookery is where many birds build their nests in the trees.

Three different mangroves grow along Florida's coasts. The red mangrove trees are closest to the water's edge. Their long prop roots reach from the branches down into the water. Black mangroves grow among the red mangroves. They have pneumatophores, which are breathing tubes that stick up from their roots. The pneumatophores work like snorkels so the tree can breathe in waterlogged soil. White mangroves grow farther away from the water. Their thick, rounded leaves have two little glands at the base.

Flooding *by Desiree Companion*

Flooding is part of the earth's natural hydrological cycle. Floodplains are low-lying areas near coastlines, rivers and streams that temporarily store excess surface water caused by storm surge or intense rainfalls. Many people want to live by water, and their homes and businesses have filled these once-natural storage systems. Flooding only becomes a problem when met with human habitation.

Residential Development *by Curtis Porterfield*

When people build, they often get rid of natural lands and surface water to make room for the buildings and roads. This means that many animals and plants lose their homes. Surface water refills ground water. When we get rid of surface water, we lose ground water too. When surface waters are surrounded by buildings and roads, they change. Dirty substances can run off into surface waters when it rains, and this can make the waters too dirty for plants and animals to live in.

Dredging *by Dr. Charles O'Connor*

A dredge is a machine used to deepen or straighten a waterway. This can speed boat traffic and water movement, but many problems can occur. Pollution in the mud can spread. The water can become muddy and not as friendly to life. Fish, plants and birds can be harmed by quick changes. The plants and fish may die and then the birds have a problem finding food. Fast-flowing water is in less contact with plants that help clean the water. Usually, nature changes waterways more slowly so that life can adjust. Some waterways that were dredged are now being restored and repaired.

Canals *by Dr. Charles O'Connor*

Canals are dug for many reasons, often to drain water off the land. During Florida's wet season, storms dump great amounts of rain. Roads and buildings can be flooded. Unfortunately, canals speed this rainwater into the ocean. This causes a number of problems. This water is no longer available to nourish plants and animals. It no longer can soak deep into the ground to restore our supply of underground water in the aquifer. If our aquifer water level becomes too low, saltwater intrusion may occur when the ocean is able to push salt water into the aquifer, making it unfit for drinking or agriculture. Too much water channeled through canals to our estuaries can also alter the health of this important ecosystem.

Florida Gulf Refuges *by Carol Mahler*

Beginning in the early 1900s, many mangrove islands in Lee and Charlotte counties were set aside as wildlife refuges to protect these areas for roosting and nesting birds. Matlacha Pass National Wildlife Refuge includes 23 islands between Pine Island and Cape Coral. The other four refuges are Island Bay National Wildlife Refuge, Pine Island National Wildlife Refuge, Caloosahatchee National Wildlife Refuge and the "Ding" Darling National Wildlife Refuge on Sanibel Island. "Ding" Darling has public access and a nature center.

Section 1: Banana Creek Marsh

A mother alligator pushes leaves, sticks and mud together. Dark clouds block the sun as lightning flashes and thunder booms. The alligator shapes the pile into a mound for her nest.

When the moon rises, the mother climbs on top of the nest. She digs into it with her back legs and lays her eggs, burying them. The eggs are kept warm by the heat produced from the rotting plants.

In July and August, the mother guards her nest. In September, she hears a chirping sound. Her babies are hatching and call her to dig them out. She claws the nest. As the babies crawl out of the eggs, she gathers them in her mouth and carries them to the lake. She makes many trips.

One baby alligator is late. It breaks out of its egg and chirps, but its mother is too far away to hear.

Then the hatchling is lifted into the air. A young woman holds the alligator closely behind its head so it cannot turn and bite.

"Well, little one, what are you doing here?"

The woman holds a clipboard under her left arm.

continued

Section 1: Banana Creek Marsh (*continued*)

"I can see your nest. That's a lot of eggs! This marsh must be working. In the 1940s, a canal was dug to drain the land. A few years ago, it was filled in. Now water covers the pasture where cattle once grazed. You were born in a Polk County park named after the old ranch, the Circle B Bar Reserve."

The baby alligator stops wiggling.

"I can see your mother's tracks. I guess she forgot you, so I'll carry you." The woman starts walking. Her boots slurp in the wet ooze.

"I'll bet you're wondering about me, aren't you? My job is to count whatever wildlife I see. Around the lake are other cattle ranches and orange groves — even some houses. More houses are being built every day. Lake Hancock is one of the most polluted lakes in Florida, but it's getting better." Near the lakeshore, the woman stops. She stretches out her arm. "There's your mother — see?" Then she pulls the baby alligator near again. "I don't want to get close enough to meet your mother! But I'm happy we met. Your scientific name is *Alligator mississippiensis*, but I'll call you Missy. Bye, Missy."

On the ground, Missy scoots toward her mother.

— Florida law prohibits feeding, disturbing or capturing alligators. —

Section 2: Lake Hancock

In the lake, the baby alligators crowd around their mother. Two other mothers with their babies join the pod. The pod may stay together for as long as two years. The babies eat tadpoles and minnows. They learn to catch snails, dragonflies and frogs.

Near shore, Missy floats. Only her snout and the top of her back show. She feels the water moving as a fish swims by. It shimmers. She lunges with open jaws, but the fish darts away.

As Missy chases it, she swims into the lake. Watching the fish, Missy doesn't see the osprey's shadow. The bird dives and seizes her in its talons.

They soar into the sky. Suddenly, Missy can see the tops of oaks and cypresses. The lake shrinks into a shape, as round as a possum curled up. Peace River is its tail. But between the body and the tail is a dam. The osprey tightens its grip, yet none of the talons pierce Missy. Shrill cries ring in the air. As the osprey dips toward the lake, an eagle swoops toward them with talons outstretched.

The osprey turns and dives lower, over the dam. Its cries are harsh and shrill. The eagle calls out. It circles and flies toward them to attack. Above the river, the osprey releases Missy. It turns with talons up and open to meet the attacker. The sound of their screeches echo in the rushing wind as Missy falls.

Splash! She slowly sinks to the bottom of the river and stays under until the osprey and eagle have flown away. Then she glides along the sandy river bottom.

Section 3: Peace River

Missy is an easy target on the white sand of the riverbank. So she crawls under a large branch in the water to hide.

Hours after sunset, the moon rises. The light wakes Missy. It seems bright enough to be the sun, but it does not warm her. She stays in the river because the water is warmer than the night air.

A barred owl asks, "Who?" The crickets chirp. The owl asks again. Another owl hoots. Soon, they cackle at each other, their voices echoing across the night air.

Then Missy hears movement. Soon, she smells a raccoon. It is on the branch she is hiding under. The raccoon's weight has shifted the branch, and Missy is caught. The branch sinks deeper into the water. Then the twigs push her to the sandy river bottom.

Even underwater, Missy can hear the raccoon grab for a fish. Again and again, Missy feels the same motion. When the raccoon catches something, the sounds change. Although she is trapped, she is also safe from the raccoon.

At last, the raccoon leaves, and Missy is free.

Section 4: Peace River Park

   Swimming downstream, Missy enters a swamp. Bald cypress trees stand tall above the water. Streamers of Spanish moss hang from their branches.

   An egret perches on a cypress knee. It dips into the water and catches a mosquito fish. Missy eats one too. The fish, as small as a guppies, eat the larvae of mosquitoes.

continued

Section 4: Peace River Park *(continued)*

A hurricane in 2004 blew down branches and trees. Missy hides beneath one and another as the ground becomes more mud than water. She follows the rise of the land toward the scent of sun-baked sand and plants.

Missy wiggles through Virginia creeper and swamp fern. She sees a sidewalk. Across the road is a tall hill. It is taller than the riverbank or a cypress tree.

Missy hears footsteps and dogs panting. She hides in the ferns.

A woman holds her son's hand. She tells him, "That big hill where we parked used to be a clay settling pond from a phosphate mine. It's dried up now, but when it was first made, the watery stuff inside it was really yucky."

A man holding the leashes of two dogs says, "Pardon me, ma'am. It's what they now call reclaimed." The dogs pull toward the boy. "Don't worry. These dogs won't hurt you."

Then he turns to the mother.

"The hill's planted in grass, and it makes a big, open field. The dogs love it."

The dogs sniff the ground, pulling against their leashes. They whine toward Missy. She holds still.

The man says, "You should walk the boardwalk. It winds through the swamp to the river."

She says, "There's only about an hour of daylight left."

"You have time to walk to the river. You'll want to stop and look at everything. You can even see the high-water mark on the tree trunks." The man pulls on the leashes. The dogs bark and whine and tug harder.

"I will — thanks." She smiles at him.

He yanks the leashes. "C'mon, boys," he says to the dogs.

Before she turns to the river, Missy waits until the footsteps fade away.

Section 5: Fort Meade Recreational Park

For centuries, people have crossed Peace River at Fort Meade. Today, U.S. Highway 98 bridges the river, and hickory trees grow on the banks. As Missy passes under the bridge, a nut falls near her. When it rises to the surface, she bats it down. It pops up again as they float together.

At the boat ramp, three men are fishing. One rests the end of his fishing pole on the ground. A bream dangles at the end of his line. "So far, only stumpknockers — and too small to keep," he says.

He works the hook free and tosses the fish. It lands in the water not far from Missy. The fish is the right size for her. She dives and catches it in her teeth. She drags it up on the bank beneath a tangle of twigs. She tears it into chunks as she eats it.

Another man catches a fish and the pole bends. He reels it in. The fish sways at the end of his line. "Look here — a walking catfish."

A third man says, "You're kidding. I didn't think they'd gotten this far north." He sips coffee from a Styrofoam cup with a plastic cover.

The man with the catfish says, "I've been catching them for years. I remember back in the 1960s when they first got loose. It was from a fish farm or truck north of Miami."

"I hear they'll eat anything." The third man sips his coffee again.

"Sure enough. And they can live in the muddiest water. And they'll eat everything in a puddle and then walk to the next one," the first man explains.

The man slips off the plastic cover, drains the last of the coffee and then fits the top on again. He walks up the ramp, tosses it into a trash can and then returns. "You gonna let him go?"

"No way — tastes just like a regular old Florida catfish — maybe better." Wearing a glove, he holds the fish. He slips the hook from its mouth. He tosses it into a bucket half full of water. Drops splash all around.

Missy swallows the last bit of fish. She dives into the river and moves south with the current.

Section 6: Pioneer Park

Missy passes an oak tree that curves into the water. At first, it seems that a branch is moving. But it is a water moccasin! Quickly, Missy swims away.

She dives between the twigs of a submerged branch. The snake pushes through just behind her. She swims to the bottom and wiggles beneath a sunken log. She surprises a snapping turtle, hiding in the mud, waiting to catch a fish.

The turtle swims up.

It blocks the snake's path, and the snake turns away. It moves as easily as a ripple of water.

Later, Missy drifts beside a floating branch under the twin bridges of U.S. Highway 17 in Zolfo Springs.

They mark the north end of Pioneer Park. A nature trail leads from the pavilion to the boat ramp. Two women walk as fast as the current carries Missy.

One asks, "Have you been inside the Cracker Trail Museum?"

"Not yet," the other one says. "My husband and I walked around last evening when we arrived. We saw the blacksmith shop, post office and the Hart Cabin. I can't believe that it was built in 1879!"

"I know what you mean." She laughs.

"We also walked by the Hardee County Animal Refuge, but it was closed. Have you been inside?"

"It's great. They have animals that are hard to see in the wild — a panther and a black bear."

"Do they have alligators?"

She laughs. "I see alligators all the time, but not in the refuge." She sweeps her arm from side to side. "Just look at the river."

The other woman sees and points at Missy. "There's a little one!"

"You're right! And I don't know that I've ever seen one that small."

"That's the first one I've seen — and I'm happy it's a baby."

The women turn away from the river at the boat ramp. Two men unload canoes. A group of boys and their fathers stand near. They zip on life vests and hold paddles. Beside them are coolers, tents and other gear.

As Missy swims under the S.R. 64 bridge, she leaves the park.

Section 7: Peace River Canoe Trail

The canoes catch up with Missy. First, she hears talking and laughing and the dip of paddles. Then, one paddle thunks the side of the canoe.

She floats beside a branch in the grassy water. The canoes close in.

"Hey — look over there," a man says, pointing to her. "It's a baby alligator."

"Cool, man," another says. "It's so small."

"Look, Daddy," a boy holds up a plastic alligator. "It looks just like my toy."

The boy's father scoops Missy into a net. "Let's have some fun."

Missy struggles. He holds the netting with one hand and the handle with the other, trying to dump her into the canoe. He shakes harder. The claws of one foot tangle in the net. She dangles there. He swings her lightly against the side of the canoe. Her foot twists free, and she thumps into the bottom of the canoe.

The boy pulls his feet up onto the seat. "Wow! Will it bite?"

"Yes, it will bite! Stay back!"

The boy's father watches the other canoes crowd around to watch. Throw that toy gator down. Let's see what the alligator does with it."

On the bottom of the canoe, Missy doesn't move. She stands on her three good legs. Her hurt leg throbs.

One man calls, "Heads up! We're drifting into that log jam over there."

They paddle the canoes away from the danger. One of the boys asks, "What's that gator doing?"

"Nothing," the father says. He paddles the canoe. The warmth of sun and the movement of the canoe lull Missy. Mile after mile, the canoes push south.

Missy doesn't move, so the boy watches the birds. Kingfishers zigzag from shore to shore. Egrets and herons skim above the river. The boy turns to his father, "Don't they get tired of getting surprised by us? That same white one flies away when we come close. It only goes a little way down the river. We surprise it again and again. How come it doesn't get tired of doing that?"

"I don't know, son, but I'm tired of this gator. It might as well have been a toy too." Reaching down, he grabs Missy by the tail and flips her overboard.

She swims as fast as she can away from the canoes.

Section 8: Brownville Park

Beside a branch, Missy floats under the bridge for Brownville Road. Just south of it is Brownville Park. She watches a woman and a teenage girl in kayaks.

"Remember the time when the water was so low?" the woman asks.

"We had our canoe then. I was very young," her daughter says.

"It was a drought. Didn't we have to get out and walk across the sandy places?"

"But it wasn't sandy, Mom. It was yucky. We sank in up to our knees."

The mother laughs. "I do remember. We were so happy to find some deeper water to wash that muck off our legs."

Soon they are far away. Missy floats along the west shore. Vines with heart-shaped leaves seem to smother the trees. On the vines are small growths that look like brown potatoes. The vines make a dense shade, so no other plants grow beneath them. Above, a panther naps on a thick oak branch.

Missy dives into the river. She surfaces at the center where a bald cypress grows. Crowded around the base of the tree are cypress knees. Part of the root system, they may help support the tree in the water. A plastic bottle, filled with sand and water, is wedged there. Many creatures hide here. As a minnow slips past her, Missy grabs and eats it. Then she moves south with the river.

Section 9:
DeSoto Veterans Park and Morgan Park

Missy swims into a hollow log. It is full of water and open on one side. A sound louder than a hundred cicadas startles a mottled duck. As it starts to fly, it seems to run across the water on its webbed feet. The humming echoes from either side of the river. Missy watches a flat-bottomed green boat skim by. Its wake rocks the log. The water sloshes inside. Missy can smell the exhaust fumes and the drips of oil from the boat engine.

Before the waves calm, the noise stops. Then Missy hears another throbbing. A truck with a trailer backs down the DeSoto Veterans Park boat ramp. Someone pushes and pulls the boat and winches it onto the trailer. As the truck drives up the ramp, water pours from the engine and boat.

Missy leaves her hiding place. She swims along the east shore. She can hear the thumping of feet. People and dogs jog and walk the trail in Morgan Park. Then she passes under the wide concrete piers for the old bridge and new bridges of S.R. 70. Cars and trucks drive to and from Arcadia.

Thick pine forests once grew on the banks. They were cut for lumber. Many trees in the Peace River Valley have been harvested or cleared away for development. In the warm shallows, Missy hunts for food. She swallows some frog eggs floating in the grasses. Then she feels movement. Cows amble into the river. As one grazes near Missy, a grasshopper flies up. Missy lunges to catch it. The cow looks at Missy and keeps eating.

Missy hears a noise like a trumpet. A sandhill crane calls. Another glides with it, and they land in the grass. Their long bills find insects to eat in the ground.

Cattle egrets also feed with the cows. They snap up bugs that the cows frighten. An egret perches on the back of a cow to eat bugs. Cow manure falls on the sand and in the water, and Missy swims away.

In places, the riverbank is steep and high. In others, the ground slopes to the water. In the early twentieth century, phosphate rock was dug from the riverbed. The sand leftover from the mining changed the shape of the banks.

Missy rests on the slope of a sandbar under a willow tree. Ridges in the sand mark the waves of water. She feels a humming, and then she hears it. An airboat skims by. It throws a spray of wind and water. It feels like rain. It chases a school of minnows toward her. Missy snaps up one, two, three!

Section 10: Lettuce Lake

Before dawn, mist swirls above the river. Near Horse Creek, Missy hides. Moonflower vines cover the trees and bushes. Across the river, two bald eagles perch in a dead tree. As Missy wriggles through a fallen branch, she stops. A deer wades into the water to drink. When it walks away, she swims on.

Where C.R. 761 bridges the river, she swims underwater. The rumbling of traffic is not so loud. South of the bridge is an island. The lights of the Peace River Water Treatment Plant shine on one side. Taking water from the river and then treating it, the plant provides water to people in DeSoto, Charlotte and Sarasota counties.

Downstream of the bridge, the river curves and widens here. Buoys mark crab traps. Near lunchtime, Missy floats close to the shore. From one fern, she grabs a green anole. A large alligator crawls onto the shore. A boat full of people turns toward them. The loud speaker echoes across the water: "Alligator to your left."

A man says, "Wow! That's the biggest one we've seen today."

Standing beside him, another says, "I'd say a good 12 feet."

Many people hold cameras. As the boat nudges the shore, the alligator slides into the river.

continued

Section 10: Lettuce Lake (*continued*)

"There he goes, folks, straight to the bottom. I hope you got a good shot of him," the loudspeaker says. The engine clunks into reverse. The boat shudders again and turns upriver.

Missy stays away from the big alligator and the boats. She swims south along the shore. Crowding out the large ferns and river grasses are Brazilian pepper trees. Above them, a red-shouldered hawk perches in a dead tree. Missy ducks beneath some water lily pads. They only grow here when the river's flow keeps the salt water in the harbor.

Then her foot catches a plastic shopping bag. She pulls, but it is stuck. She tries swimming deeper into the water. Air caught inside the bag keeps it floating. She rips at the bag with her teeth and slips free.

The channel splits again, and she takes the east branch of the river known as Lettuce Lake, named for the plants that look like heads of lettuce. Many houseboats cluster near the boat ramp. Missy dives away from them.

She swims along the bottom of the river. She feels something large — more than one — above her. She hides near a sunken log, and manatees pass above her.

Section 11: Shell Creek

Peace River turns west where it meets Shell Creek. Upstream, the creek is dammed. It creates a reservoir for the City of Punta Gorda Water Treatment Plant. Down river, Missy floats under the bridge of Interstate 75, where six lanes of traffic zoom across.

Homes and docks line the southern shore. Soon she passes some cement picnic tables near a historic hunting and fishing lodge. It was named Eagle's Nest Lodge because a pair of eagles nested in a nearby pine tree. A woman and a man sit at a table. Missy hears the woman say, "Many famous people used to fish here."

"What did they catch?" the man asks.

She says, "The harbor was full of fish — snook, redfish, mullet."

"Has sportfishing cleaned them out?" he asks.

"Maybe. Maybe commercial fishing. I don't know," she says.

"I heard that more than 1,000 people a day move to Florida. Maybe the harbor only has room for so many living things. There used to be more fish. Now, there are more people," he says.

Missy paddles away.

Section 12: Alligator Bay

Missy wiggles through the roots of the mangroves. She follows the shore, past condominiums and houses. She swims by Laishley Park, beneath the fishing pier and past the marina. She sees anhingas perched on the power lines that span the river, as evenly spaced as beads on a string.

On the south shore is Punta Gorda. The man who founded the town gave the waterfront as a gift to the people living there. Along the river is Gilchrist Park, named for a local resident who was governor of Florida from 1911 to 1913.

Missy crosses the harbor in the shadow of the U.S. Highway 41 bridges. She moves from one piling to another. Where the water is deep, she dives. She scoots away from a huge grouper.

When she is halfway across, she hears a spray of water. A dolphin comes out of the water to breathe. Another two follow. Then a brown pelican crashes beak-first into the water to catch a fish.

Finally she reaches the north shore. Charlotte Harbor is the oldest community in Charlotte County. Cattlemen and commercial fishermen lived there. Missy swims through pilings for docks, along the shore of

Bayshore Live Oak Park and past the Charlotte County Historical Center.

Here, seawalls edge the bank. A brown palm frond shakes loose in the wind and falls on Missy. She swims beneath it for a while. Then she squirms between the fronds. Now it is her raft. In the distance, she can see the Port Charlotte Beach Complex and fishing pier. Canals and houses crowd around it. The current pushes Missy west where the shore is green. Maybe Missy has found a home in Alligator Bay.

Let's Explore Further

Alligators *by Kayton Nedza*

Alligators are reptiles. They are cold-blooded, so the sun and air temperatures adjust their bodies' heat. They lay eggs in a nest. If the temperature is hot, the eggs will be males; if the temperature is cool, they will be females. Little alligators are black with yellow stripes, which helps them blend into the shade and murky water. Many animals eat baby alligators, including raccoons, otters, herons, snakes, fish and other alligators. Babies stay with their mother for the first year or two so she can protect them. On land, an alligator can run very fast for a short distance, so you should stay away!

Alligator Behavior *by Kayton Nedza*

In addition to a regular eyelid, alligators have a transparent eyelid. Like swim goggles, it protects the eye and lets the alligator see. Alligators close their ears, which are located behind their eyes, to keep water out of them. They can also close their throats, so they can bite and chew underwater. They raise their heads above water to swallow. Small alligators eat minnows, insects, tadpoles and frogs. Large alligators eat raccoons, turtles, snakes and animals as large as a deer or Florida panther. Strong acid in their stomachs digests bones and teeth. They swallow small prey whole and will rip large prey into chunks before swallowing it. Florida law prohibits feeding, disturbing or capturing alligators.

Dams *by Diane Herron*

If trees fall where a creek is narrow, the water will puddle up. The fallen tree stops the flow until the water can find its way around or over the tree as it tries to move downward. Water in a higher place always tries to find its way into a lower place. That's why creeks and rivers flow! They are moving downward, even if the land doesn't seem to slope. If the flow of water is stopped or reduced, then everything that depended on it downstream has to adapt to less water, move away or die. Behind the dam, everything has to survive in more water. Water is so important that sometimes people build dams to store water.

Lake Hancock Dam *by Curtis Porterfield*

Lake Hancock is a 4,500-acre lake north of Bartow. A dam called the P-11 controlled the water level in the lake. It was demolished after new structures were built to maintain the level of the lake and release water to Peace River. Water released from the lake begins the Peace River. The dam does not allow animals traveling up the river to go any farther by water. When the gates of the dam are open, some small animals in the lake may go into the river. Over the years, the lake has collected a lot of pollutants from wastewater treatment plants. Some say that the lake water released into the river may be polluting the river itself.

Phosphate *by Kayton Nedza*

Phosphate is the chemical element phosphorus. Essential to life, it is in all living things. Millions of years ago, this part of Florida was ocean bottom. Currents caused the growth of many plants and animals, such as sharks, stingrays, whales and dugongs (an animal like the manatee). As these plants and animals died, their remains drifted to the bottom and the phosphorus in their bodies turned into phosphate. In the late 1800s, people started mining phosphate to make fertilizer. Today, Florida phosphate companies produce approximately 57 percent of the phosphate fertilizer used in the United States and 17 percent of the phosphate used to grow the world's food supply.

Phosphate Mining *by Kayton Nedza*

Today, phosphate mines are strip mines. The dirt over the phosphate is moved out of the way and the phosphate is dug up. Some of the large leftover holes are reclaimed as lakes, and engineered earthen dams store clay particles separated from the phosphate. Like agriculture, power-generating utilities and cities, the phosphate industry consumes much ground water and may have helped cause Kissingen Springs to dry up during the 1950s. Before 1975, when stricter laws were passed, some mined land was not reclaimed, and several spills polluted the Peace River and some tributaries. Today, the industry must meet state and federal water quality standards. It has dramatically reduced its water usage, recycling 95 percent of water at mining sites. Reclaimed mines can be used for agriculture, parks, wetlands, lakes and housing developments. Some of the land has been donated so the public can enjoy the Peace River, public fishing lakes and parks.

Exotics and Invasive Exotics *by Melissa Cain Nell*

If you were born in Florida, you are a "Florida native." Plants and animals can be natives, too, if they live here naturally. Plants and animals that grow naturally elsewhere but have been brought to Florida are called exotics. Often, these species have no predators or other environmental controls and they quickly multiply and take over. When an exotic competes with native plants and animals for food, water, shelter and space, it is called an invasive species. Because of its tropical climate, Florida is a paradise for exotic species, such as the Brazilian pepper tree, melaleuca tree, air potato vine, pasture grass, hydrilla, water hyacinth, wild hog, iguana, European starling, house sparrow, walking catfish and fire ants.

Beef Cattle *by Kayton Nedza*

In the 1500s, Spaniards brought beef cattle to Florida. By the late 1700s, the Seminole Indians had the largest herds. During the Civil War, in the 1860s, the Peace River Valley supplied beef cattle to the Confederate Army. During the 1890s, cowmen fought "range wars" for cattle ownership and those times were wilder than the "wild west." Today, Florida is one of the top 12 states that supply cattle for beef. Many ranches fence cows from swamps and riverbanks, and they burn the grasslands as part of a natural cycle of fire. Many acres of ranches are native Florida lands, which serve as wildlife habitat.

Visible Pollution *by Anita Forester*

Sometimes you can see pollution in a river, such as plastic bags, fishing lines, soda cans, glass bottles, tires or old tools. Some animals may think that pollution is food, but when they try to eat it, they get sick. Other pollution can trap animals or plants so they can't move or grow, and pollution can also kill animals and plants. Many people who use the river collect litter that they find. Local communities also host "river cleanup" days to help the river, and everyone can pick up litter in the river and on the land.

Salinity *by Curtis Porterfield*

Salinity measures the saltiness of water. Many chemicals can be salts, but the most familiar one is the salt used on foods known as sodium chloride. All water has some salt, because as water moves, it picks up salt from the ground. Rivers, lakes and streams are fresh water, which is not very salty. Estuaries are where fresh water meets the sea. Their waters are often called brackish, which is saltier than fresh water. The sea is salt water and has a lot of salt in it. The saltiness of the water affects where aquatic plants and animals live. Some animals and plants like salty water, so they live in the sea or estuaries. Others don't like salty water, so they only live in fresh water.

Chapter 3
Myakka River

Section 1: Myakka Head

Two otters explore a dead hollow tree. Half its trunk is on the shore; the other half is in Myakka River. They swim into the hollow from underneath. Inside, they climb above the water. The space is dry, and air comes through holes made by woodpeckers. It is a perfect den, and the mother gives birth to three kits.

Three weeks later, the mother and father begin teaching them to swim and to catch food. At three months old, the otters could live without their parents, but the children may stay with their parents for two years.

One day in June, it rains, and the otters play. Leaves and sticks are slick with wetness, so the otters make a slide on the riverbank. Crayfish scuttle from the rising river. The otters make a game of catching and eating them.

It rains and rains. Their den is flooded inside, so the otters sit outside. A young otter dives for a fish, and the father scolds. Otters are good swimmers, but the current is too strong, and it carries the otter downstream.

Dressed in rain slickers, two men stand near a pickup truck. They watch the Myakka River flow over S.R. 64. The otter hears them talking.

"I can't remember flooding like this," a man says.

"Summer of 1992, it was so bad that they closed S.R. 70," a second man says.

The second man says, "Hey, look! There's an otter. A little one."

The first man says, "Probably not quite a full-grown *Lutra canadensis*."

"A what?" the second man asks.

"*Lutra canadensis* is the scientific name for the North American river otter," the first man says.

"I'll call her Lu, for short." The second man tugs on his cap. "Hey, Lu. You'd better go under rather than over the highway."

Even as the man speaks, Lu dives into the current. It rushes her under the highway. She surfaces on the other side.

The man claps his hands. "Nice going, Lu. Enjoy your swim!"

Section 2: Flatford Swamp

The current slows as the river enters Flatford Swamp. Water spreads across the low-lying ground. Sand Slough meets six creeks here: Ogleby Creek, Boggy Creek, Coker Creek, Young's Creek, Long Creek and Maple Creek.

A man and a boy stand together where Myakka Road crosses Taylor Road. The water almost covers their knee-high rubber boots. Lu rests at one end of a log. Her dark-brown fur matches the log's color. An ibis stands on the other end. Lu hears the people talking.

"Wow, Daddy. Was it ever like this? I mean, when you were a boy?"

"Yes, the river flooded, but the swamp was shady then, just full of trees!" the man says.

The boy asks, "What happened to them?"

"They died. You can see the trunks and stumps. Folks say too much water killed the trees. Some have fallen, too, like that log where the ibis just landed."

"How can water kill a tree?" The boy brushes a deer fly from his arm.

"A tree needs time when the land is dry. You know how you kids say you want to stay in the pool all day, but you want some time to dry out too?"

"Yeah. So why did the trees stay wet?" the boy asks.

Lu watches a damselfly.

"Ranchers around here used to run cattle. Then about 20 years ago, some planted crops, like tomatoes and watermelons. In the dry season, they watered them, and the water that the plants didn't use ran into the swamp. It was wet all the time, so the trees started dying."

continued

Section 2: Flatford Swamp *(continued)*

The damselfly lands on the log near Lu.

The boy looks around. "But I see some trees."

"That's because some farmers are using a new system. It keeps water in the fields and out of the swamp."

The boy says, "That sounds good!"

The damselfly skims the water. A bass strikes it.

"I think it will help the swamp. Maybe the farmers too. It costs a lot in the beginning, but using it over and over will make watering the crops cheaper."

Lu watches a bluegill caught for a moment against the log.

The boy points to the log as Lu glides into the water. "Hey, Daddy, that log's moving."

Lu catches the fish and eats it as she moves away.

Section 3: Myakka City Park

The river has flooded Myakka City Park. Three black vultures perch on the dead branches of an oak tree. A white egret stands on a picnic table and watches a green plastic soda bottle float by.

The swings in the park are underwater. Lu finds the black-rubber swings pulling downstream on their chains and swims against one. She feels how it holds her belly as she moves over it. The swing turns suddenly and flips her upstream. She dives and flips again.

Crossing the bridge, a mother pulls a red wagon. Two girls sit inside the wagon. The five-year-old sits in back and has her arms around her sister, who sits between her legs.

The mother pulls the wagon onto the shoulder of the road. She points to Lu. "Look, girls, an otter is playing on one of the swings."

"Oh, I want to play," the older girl says.

"Me too," her little sister says.

Their mother warns, "Don't be silly, you can't play in a flooded river. It's dangerous. The current is very strong, and all kinds of things get in the river — trash and animal dung. Big limbs and other things can hit you."

The mother watches a red and white plastic cooler. It is caught in the branches of a willow. Now the current pulls it free. She points. "There's someone's cooler. It's floating like a boat."

"It looks just like ours, Mama," the older girl says.

"It's going to hit the otter," her sister says.

The woman calls, "Watch out, otter!"

continued

Section 3: Myakka City Park *(continued)*

Lu has already dived into the river. The cooler floats above her. She swims with the current under the S.R. 70 bridge.

Section 4: Tatum Sawgrass Marsh

Beneath the bridge for S.R. 780, the river flows fast. A large branch is lodged against
a bridge support. The water dammed behind it hardly moves. Lu swims there to rest. Branches from a swamp maple
overhang the river.

Above her, a man and woman watch a swallow-tailed kite soar above Tatum
Sawgrass Marsh. The man swings his arm
in a wide arc. "Imagine all the water it took to fill the marsh. It's a lake now. I'm
guessing that water covers the boardwalk
at Crowley Museum and Nature Center."

The woman says, "Years ago, they drained this marsh and planted all kinds of nonnative grass for cattle."

"I'll bet it didn't look like this back then," the man says.

They both laugh.

"When we canoed it, we saw those grasses growing like a wall along some places. Except for there, it looked like a scenic river. Now it looks wild," the woman says.

continued

Section 4: Tatum Sawgrass Marsh *(continued)*

"Maybe that's why they call it a 'Wild and Scenic River,' " the man says.

The woman asks, "What does that mean?"

The man says, "The U.S. and Florida legislatures chose the name to tell everybody that a river is special. Florida has two National Wild and Scenic Rivers, but Myakka is the only Florida Wild and Scenic River."

Lu sees a tree frog as green as a leaf. She eats it.

The woman asks, "What does it need to be protected from?"

"Houses built near the river," the man answers.

"Houses don't hurt the river," the woman says.

"Clearing the land to build them does. Rain can wash sand into the river. Drilling wells, burying septic tanks, making seawalls and docks — it all damages the river. Even drips of oil from roads can wash into the water."

Lu sees a peninsula cooter. She dives below, circles and grabs the turtle.

"But look at this flood." The woman points to the river on both sides of the bridge. "It's doing more to harm the river than building a few houses."

The man says, "Having more water in the river doesn't harm it. The river is alive, so the water can be high or low or even change its banks. It's what people do or don't do beside the river that can hurt it."

Lu paddles back into the current.

Section 5:
Upper Myakka Lake

At the end of Upper Myakka Lake, Lu finds a weir — a concrete wall across the lower end of the lake. When the river is low, the weir holds water in the lake. When the river is high, water flows over it.

The sides slope and are worn smooth from more than 70 years of the river washing it. For Lu, it forms a perfect slide. She climbs to the top of one end and, on her belly, she glides into the water. Her sleek body makes no splash.

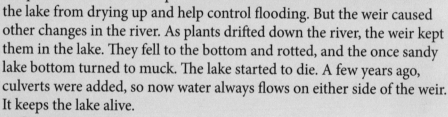

The Civilian Conservation Corps built the weir to keep the lake from drying up and help control flooding. But the weir caused other changes in the river. As plants drifted down the river, the weir kept them in the lake. They fell to the bottom and rotted, and the once sandy lake bottom turned to muck. The lake started to die. A few years ago, culverts were added, so now water always flows on either side of the weir. It keeps the lake alive.

Common grackles crowd a water oak. Their iridescent plumage sparkles as they chirrup, flutter and change places. They seem as busy and noisy as a group of children. Suddenly, they rise into the air. They swoop over Lu playing in the water. She stops to watch them. The grackles scatter for a moment and then gather. They circle and settle again in the tree.

Lu watches a great blue heron standing like a statue in the shallows. When it sees a fish, it spears it. Tipping its beak up, it tosses and catches the fish headfirst so it is easier to swallow.

To Lu, this looks like a game. She spies a golden shiner, dives and catches it in her mouth. Crawling up the shore, she flips her head up and opens her mouth. The fish flies into the air, and she catches it. She does it again and again.

An osprey swoops above, hoping to steal the fish. But Lu quickly eats it and then swims downstream.

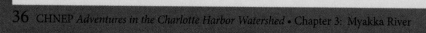

Section 6: Lower Myakka Lake

Flooding has closed Myakka River State Park. The river is full of floating water hyacinths and hydrilla. Lu can't swim through the plants piled up beneath the S.R. 72 bridge. She climbs the bank and scampers across the road. Before a car drives by, she dives into the river.

The land south of the highway is Myakka River State Park Wilderness Preserve. People must have a permit to explore any part of these 7,600 acres, but not Lu. She swims in and out of tree branches and trunks that used to stand and hang over the water. When she leaps over one, she looks as graceful as a dolphin.

Leaves, sticks and many other things float in the river. Where the water is too murky, Lu's whiskers find the way. When they brush a crayfish, she catches and crunches it.

She climbs onto a large oak limb. Resurrection ferns grow like fur along it. Spanish moss dangles above and a tree frog hangs in it. Its tongue snaps a mosquito. Lu lunges for the frog, but it jumps into the water. Then a water snake strikes from beneath the branch and swallows the frog.

What seems to be a log veers at the snake, but Lu sees an alligator.

She turns. On a branch beyond her is a limpkin. It dips its beak into a groove of the oak's bark, plucks out an apple snail and eats it. Above, a butterfly orchid grows on the bark of the oak.

Lu dives into the river. It soon widens into Lower Myakka Lake. At the southern end of the lake, she feels the bottom drop away. She is swimming above a natural sinkhole now filled with water. It is called Deep Hole. When the river is low, the lake dries up except here. Deep Hole is home for the alligators.

Section 7: Carlton Reserve

South of Deep Hole, the river narrows and turns. Then it becomes wide because of a concrete dam. Lu easily swims over it. To the west of the river is the T. Mabry Carlton Jr. Memorial Reserve. A water plant there treats millions of gallons a day for people in
Sarasota County. The water does not come from the river. It is pumped from the aquifer, an
underground river.

The reserve is 24,565 acres, with more than 80 miles of hiking trails. The Reserve's "public park" has a picnic area, visitor's center and interpretive nature trails. The rest is wilderness area, and people must have a back-country permit to hike, bike or ride horses there.

Lu has traveled the river, and people can too. Or, they can walk. The Myakka-Carlton trail starts at the north entrance of Myakka River State Park, crosses the Myakka Prairie and ends in the Carlton Reserve.

Lu sees a black bear in a tree, where the trunk grows into three wide branches. One limb curves into the water. Dead palm fronds, sticks and leaves are trapped there. So is a bass. The bear leans into the water and grabs it. Water drips from its fur as it eats the fish.

Downriver, Lu explores a willow thicket. Caught on the twigs are fern fronds, pasture grasses, Spanish moss and a piece of window screen. The current pulls it against the branches, forming a net. A redear sunfish struggles inside.

Lu pushes her head into the net and grabs the fish. Then she can't move because the current pushes her into the net. Her sharp teeth and claws rip at the screen. It breaks from the branches on one side, freeing her to eat the fish.

Section 8: Snook Haven

Soon Lu hears the rumble of traffic on the bridges for Interstate 75. To escape the noise, she swims under the water.

Branches, leaves and other debris pile up against the bridge piers. She twists and turns through the maze. She holds her breath a long time to swim under the bridges. When she rises to the surface, she breathes deeply and paddles to keep herself safe in the current.

Where the river curves, she can see buildings. Under oak trees, two men stand on a deck filled with picnic tables. Mosquitoes and gnats fly in a cloud around their heads. Water covers the feet of their rubber boots as they lean against the railing. Lu hears them talking.

"I don't know how much more the river will rise," the first man says.

"If it's no more than this, you'll be okay," the second man says.

The first man slaps a mosquito on his arm. "It'll be a mess to clean up."

Above Lu, nighthawks dip and soar.

The second man fans the bugs away from his face. "I'll bet it's not the first time Snook Haven has seen a flood."

"You're right about that. It was here for more than half a century before Sarasota County bought it. People came here to fish and stay in the cabins. Others rented canoes or boats or took the boat tour to see the river."

The second man points to the river. "What's that?"

The first man says, "Fire ants! Stay away! When their nests are flooded, they gather into a ball and float on a branch or something. They'll latch onto anything they bump up against — even people."

Lu watches a nighthawk swoop to eat a mosquito.

The second man watches the ants float downstream. "I heard two movies were filmed here."

"That's right. The most famous one was a Tarzan movie filmed in 1938 that featured killer turtles. Some of the monkeys that escaped still live around here. Most people see them across there." The first man points

across the river.

The second man points at Lu. "Hey, there's one in the river!"

The first man chuckles. He says, "That's not a monkey. That's a river otter."

Section 9: Jelks Family Preserve

Downstream in Jelks Preserve, Lu rests on a picnic table near the river. Water flows beneath. In an oak tree above, two squirrels chase along a branch. In another tree, a mockingbird sings. First it trills like a meadowlark. Then it chirps like a wren.

She hears some splashing and footsteps. Then she watches two women wearing raincoats and boots walk along the path, which is as wide as a road. A pileated woodpecker swoops in front of them as they stop at the water's edge.

"I can't believe how high the river is," the first woman says.

"Remember when we came here a few weeks ago? We saw a gopher tortoise on the trail and a rabbit was eating grass over there." The second woman points to the table where Lu is. The woman doesn't see Lu because the otter's brown fur blends with the wet wood.

"It was a lovely evening, as I recall. The river didn't seem to move. It reflected everything, like a mirror."

"At least until those boats came speeding by," the second woman says.

"That's right! And as the waves washed in, I could see some freshwater mussels. But the clam shells surprised me."

Two doves land on the picnic table. They peck at the leaves, twigs and acorn shells. Lu watches.

The first woman says, "They call this part of the river 'Coastal Lower Myakka' because the harbor's salt water mixes with the river's fresh water."

The second woman says, "But the river flows into the harbor in Charlotte County. It seems a long way from where we are in Sarasota County."

"And lucky for us. This 600-acre preserve is a Sarasota County park, thanks to Dr. Mary Jelks. To buy the land, she gave money and asked others to donate. She even convinced the county to help."

Lu lunges toward the doves. They flutter away with soft noises, and she slides into the river.

Section 10: Myakka State Forest

Several miles downstream, Lu sees another picnic table in the Myakka State Forest. The state forest is 8,532 acres within the City of North Port.

A grill near the table is full of water, and Lu sees a small turtle swimming inside. She catches it and sits on top of the grill to eat it. She hears grunting and digging under the oaks. A family of wild hogs pushes through to the edge of the water. The mother drinks, as the piglets splash around her. They are descendants of pigs that the Spanish brought to Florida 500 years ago. From her perch, Lu sees how the pigs have rooted up the soil and plants.

continued

Section 10: Myakka State Forest *(continued)*

A Florida scrub-jay glides by. Lu watches it land on a saw palmetto. The trunk is black where a fire burned. A black beetle crawling there is almost hidden, but the jay catches and eats the bug. Once called the Florida jay, it lives only in this state. The jay needs scrub oaks and scrub pines to live, and fire helps the trees survive. Many trees have been cleared away for roads, houses and orange groves. Winchester Boulevard passes through this forest, so a sign there warns "Scrub-Jay Crossing."

At the edge of the Myakka State Forest, the river widens. Lu misses the oaks and palms that grew on its banks upstream. She sees an island covered with mangroves in this wide part of the river. It is a rookery for wood storks.

Lu swims to the island. A stork is watching. It flaps its wings and sounds an alarm. Other birds see the otter.

The birds know that otters eat bird eggs and baby birds. Several storks soar above, and others perch on the low branches of mangroves. They don't want Lu near their rookery, and they swoop toward her. She turns away from their sharp beaks and dives deep into the river.

Section 11:
El Jobean

Not far from shore, a boy with a fishing pole stands on the pier. Sitting in a folding chair beside him, his mother holds a pole too. His father baits and casts four poles and leans them against the railing.

Underwater, Lu sees crayfish on the hooks. She climbs the riverbank and then crawls onto the pier. She hears the boy say, "Hey, Mom. Joey told me that this pier once burned."

"Part of it did. The county was going to tear it down but people asked them to rebuild it because it's such a good fishing pier," the mom says.

"The railroad built this trestle for trains on their way to Boca Grande," the mom says.

"Why? So people could swim and find shells?" the boy asks.

His mother laughs. "Sometimes. But they made money by hauling phosphate. At the south end of Boca Grande, it was loaded onto big ships."

Lu creeps beside a bucket full of bait. Black flies buzz around it.

"Where did the phosphate come from?" the boy asks.

"Somewhere up the Peace River," the mom says.

"Why didn't they ship it from some place closer?" the boy asks.

"The river's too shallow. Ships need deep water," the mom says.

Lu thrusts her head into the bucket and eats a crayfish.

The boy pulls his line from the water. "Hey, Dad! I caught a crab!"

The father grabs the net and runs to the boy. "Pull it up before it lets go."

The boy yanks the pole up. The blue crab drops, but the father swings the net and catches it.

The mother cries, "Good teamwork!"

Lu eats another crayfish and another.

The father tells the boy, "Bring the bucket over here. I'll get this crab out of the net." The crab clacks its claws as it struggles to get free.

continued

Section 11: El Jobean *(continued)*

The boy sees Lu dive into the river with a crayfish in her mouth. He carries the bucket to his father. The father shakes the crab loose from the net, and it falls into the bucket. Beneath the pier, Lu eats the crayfish.

"I can't believe the size of this crab," the father says.

"It's probably all we'll catch tonight," the boy says.

"Why is that?" the mother asks.

"Because something ate all the bait," the boy says."

You're kidding! What was it?" the mother asks.

The boy says, "I don't know. It was brown, had whiskers like a cat and a long, thick tail."

The father says, "Sounds like an otter. Other fishermen have complained about otters stealing bait and fish."

Lu swims under the pier and the bridge for S.R. 776.

Section 12: Tippecanoe Bay

On the eastern shore, Lu sees mangroves. A fox squirrel sits on a branch and a reddish egret wades near the roots.

She turns away from the shore and swims into deep water. She can feel the push of the current. Then she sees a sawfish swimming toward her. Using her strong tail, she steers into Tippecanoe Bay. The sawfish does not chase her as she swims into the shallow water at the mouth of Sam Knight Creek.

On the bay is Tippecanoe Environmental Park, 380 acres owned by Charlotte County. People can enjoy the nature trails that include a boardwalk through the mangroves and marshes.

It is evening when Lu swims into a creek under the oaks. She hears buzzing and sees a wasp. It flies to a nest hanging from a limb. Grapevines curl through the branches. Near the ground, the vines are as thick as an otter's tail. Cabbage palms stand together and among the oaks.

A strangler fig grows around one tree as if it were hugging it. Lu hears tapping and sees a red-bellied woodpecker pecking at the trunk. Underneath, a skunk digs in the leaf mold for a palmetto bug. A centipede runs past a raccoon holding a crayfish. Crayfish is Lu's favorite food, so maybe Lu has found a home.

Let's Explore Further

Otters *by Diane Herron*

Otters are active mammals — eating, playing, running and swimming any time of day or night. They move from place to place but will return to a favorite spot. Sometimes, they make stick homes near ponds that they plan to return to, but these are only temporary or "vacation homes." Otters seem to be fun-loving and playing all the time, but they can bite and scratch when they need to defend themselves. In or out of the water, they eat fish, frogs, crayfish, turtles, muskrats and even baby alligators. Female otters give birth to one to five blind, furry babies, which will grow to be three or four feet.

Agriculture *by Curtis Porterfield*

Agriculture is growing food. In Florida, citrus trees are planted in groves, and fruits and vegetables are planted on farms. To make these plants grow well, farmers fertilize them. To make sure bugs don't eat them, farmers spray them with pesticides. When it rains, fertilizers and pesticides get washed into the surface water and ground water. One problem is that fertilizers will make water plants and algae grow so well that they crowd out other living things. Another problem is that pesticides can hurt some animals. Many farms and groves move, store and use water to the advantage of the plants. This may reduce the supply of ground water and cause other problems.

Invisible Pollution *by Anita Forester*

Sometimes you can't see pollution in the water. Oil, gas and other fluids from car engines can leak onto the roads, and the rain washes them into the river. Rain also washes fertilizer and pesticides that plants can't use into the river. Through natural processes, a river stays healthy by breaking down and recycling pollution back into the environment. When large amounts of pollution drain or are dumped into a river, it cannot keep up with the self-cleaning, and life in and around the river suffers. Scientists and trained volunteers check the water to detect phosphates, nitrates and other chemicals in the water. Everyone should be careful not to release chemicals into our waters!

Myakka Island *by Carol Mahler*

Islands are surrounded by water, but Myakka Island is not really an island. It is filled with water that drains into Myakka River. The land in this watershed that is natural is called Myakka Island. The state of Florida and Sarasota County own or manage some of the Myakka Island. People who own large areas of native land have given or sold conservation easements to protect the land and keep it natural. Around Myakka Island, people are building homes, roads, schools and businesses, so it has become an "island" in a sea of change.

Surface Water *by Curtis Porterfield*

Surface water is the water that can be seen on top of the land. Examples are rivers, streams, lakes, estuaries and the oceans. When it heats up, surface water evaporates and rises in the air to form clouds. Clouds release rain that replaces the surface water lost by evaporation. This is part of what is called the water cycle, and it helps to keep surface water from disappearing. Many plants and animals use surface water as both a home and a drinking water source. It is also a very important source of drinking water for people.

Land Stewardship *by Curtis Porterfield*

Land stewardship means caring for the land we live around. This can be done in many ways. One way is to keep our cities and towns clean and free of pollutants. Another way is being responsible with chemicals such as pesticides and fertilizers that can harm natural systems. A third way is to preserve and protect natural land and the plants and animals that live there. Properly caring for the land helps to keep surface and ground water clean because any harmful substances placed on the land will be washed into surface and ground water by the rain.

Ground Water *by Curtis Porterfield*

Ground water is water contained underground in aquifers. When surface water sits on top of the land, some of it leaks into the soil and deep into the ground. This ground water also moves upwards in the ground and refills surface waters. In Florida, ground water and surface water are very much connected because the bedrock (the rock beneath the soil) has many holes in it. The holes let water travel from the surface to the ground and from the ground up to the surface. Ground water is especially important to people who live in Florida because it is our main source of drinking water.

Fire *by Carol Mahler*

Sand hills, pine flatwoods, scrub and marsh need fire to live. Without fire, these areas change into another kind of habitat. For years, people have stopped natural fires started by lightning. Now, managers of wild lands start fires, called "prescribed fires" or "controlled burnings," to protect wilderness without hurting people or their property.

Endangered Species, Threatened Species, Species of Special Concern *by Carol Mahler*

Endangered species are groups of animals that may not survive because there are so few alive. Some endangered species are sea turtles, wood storks, Florida manatees and Florida panthers. People have hunted some, and pollution has killed others. Many are in danger because people have destroyed their habitats to build homes, roads, businesses, churches, schools, farms and groves. Threatened species and species of special concern are groups with more members, but their survival is also at risk for the same reasons. Some threatened species are the southern bald eagle, Florida sandhill crane, Florida scrub-jay, fox squirrel, gopher tortoise and Florida black bear. Some species of special concern are the American alligator, eastern brown pelican, reddish egret, little blue heron, tricolored heron, roseate spoonbill and limpkin.

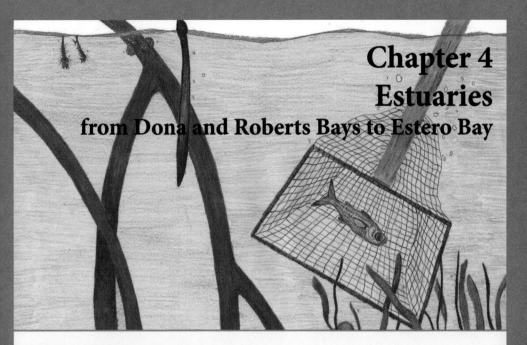

Chapter 4
Estuaries
from Dona and Roberts Bays to Estero Bay

Section 1: Lemon Bay

A baby mullet swims from the Gulf of Mexico through Stump Pass. In Lemon Bay, he keeps to the shallows where the mangroves grow. Their prop roots crisscross in the water. Big fish cannot move through the tangle of roots, so the little fish are safe.

The mullet eats tiny animals and plants. Where the water is still, he finds mosquito larvae to eat. He grows bigger.

One day, he is feeding in the seagrass near Cedar Point. A teacher from Cedar Point Environmental Center leads a wading trip. A girl scoops the mullet in a dip net and dumps him into a bucket.

The girl says, "Look! A little fish!"

The teacher looks at the fish. "That's a finger mullet, also called a fingerling."

"I grew up eating mullet," the girl's mother says.

"Let's give it a name," the girl says.

"It already has a name," the teacher says. "*Mugil cephalus*."

"That's a funny name — and hard to say too." The girl bends over the bucket and whispers to the fish, "Hello, Muggy."

"It's the scientific name for the fish. It means bullet-head or helmet-head," the teacher explains.

The teacher says to the girl and her mother, "Look for a few more minutes and then let it go."

The mother and the girl watch the fish. The girl says, "Okay, Mama, I'm ready to let it go." The mother pours out the bucket, and Muggy darts away.

"Bye, bye, Muggy," the girl says.

Section 2: Stump Pass Beach State Park

Most visitors drive on Manasota Key Road to Stump Pass Beach State Park to enjoy the Gulf beach. But Muggy swims with many other small mullet between the two islands east of Manasota Key that are also part of the park. The group of mullet is called a school, and it protects the mullet from predators because there is safety in numbers.

Muggy hears a loud noise. Then he sees a boat pass over the seagrass. The motor has a propeller that looks like the blade of a fan. It moves water instead of air. In places, the propeller cuts the seagrass. Sometimes, grass tangles around the prop and is pulled up by its roots. This kills the grass and leaves a scar, or sandy place, in the meadow of seagrass. Standing in the shallows, a little blue heron watches the school of mullet. When one mullet strays over the bare sand, the heron eats it. Muggy and the school scoot into the seagrass to hide.

The boat's motor stops, and Muggy hears voices coming from the boat.

"We can't get to Sarasota Bay from here," a woman says.

"Sure we can. But not today," a man says.

"How?" the woman asks.

The man points. "See those red and green signs in the water? They mark the Intracoastal Waterway, a deep channel made for boaters. We can follow it north to Sarasota."

continued

Section 2: Stump Pass Beach State Park *(continued)*

"How long will it take?" the woman asks.

The man says, "I'd say about an hour. First we'll go under the bridge to Englewood Beach, then through Lemon Bay and all along Manasota Key."

"That sounds like fun!" she says.

The man baits the hook on his fishing pole. "It's really fun going through Venice because the waterway is a narrow canal. On the north side of Venice, the channel goes into Roberts Bay and into Dona Bay and on up to Sarasota."

"That means the city of Venice is an island," she says.

"That's right, thanks to the Intracoastal. But most people don't think of it that way because the waterway is so narrow, and three bridges connect it to the mainland. Most islands have wider stretches of water around them."

"I can't wait to see it," she says.

"Today, I just want to fish," he says. When he casts his line, the boat rocks. A shrimp on a hook plops into the water. The school of fish zips away.

Section 3: Don Pedro Island

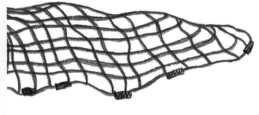

In Little Gasparilla Sound, Muggy and the school of mullet feed. Today they are in the prop roots near a fishing area of Don Pedro Island State Park.

Muggy and the other mullet hear some splashing in the water. They see the feet and legs of a man and a boy as they wade into the water. Not far from them is a school of big mullet. Some of the fish jump from the water. When they fall back into the water, they make a slapping sound.

continued

Section 3: Don Pedro Island *(continued)*

The two people stand still for a few minutes. Then the man twists as he throws a cast net. The net spreads over the water and makes an eight-foot circle. As it hits the water, the lead weights around the edges splash. Some mullet are trapped inside. Others get away before the net sinks to the bottom.

The man yanks the draw line of the net. Then he pulls the mullet through the mesh of the net and breaks the neck of each fish.

He tells the boy, "This is called 'choking' the mullet. It kills them so they can't escape. It also bleeds them, so the fillet will be white when we clean them."

Muggy watches.

"How come you don't catch mullet with a hook?" the boy asks.

The man works the net. "You can. But it takes a long time to catch as many as you can with a net. Besides, sometimes a mullet won't bite on a hook."

"Why not?" the boy asks.

The man says, "Mullet are different from most fish. They use some of the sand grains that they eat to help them grind their food. It works inside a special part of their body called a gizzard. Chickens and other birds have gizzards too."

The boy says, "Maybe that's why mullet jump! They think they can fly!"

The man laughs. "That reminds me of a story I once heard. Back in the 1920s, three fishermen were arrested for fishing for mullet out of season. In the courtroom, a biologist said that only birds have gizzards, and he said that mullet have gizzards. Then a lawyer said that if what the biologist said was true, then mullet are birds. The judge didn't believe the lawyer, but he found the fishermen not guilty."

Muggy and the school swim away.

Section 4: Cape Haze and Island Bay National Wildlife Refuge

Muggy and the school glide through mangrove roots that grow along one of the islands in Turtle Bay. Twenty acres of the mangrove shore plus some other land form the Island Bay National Wildlife Refuge.

Nearby is a fish shack built on pilings with water all around. It is a historic building because it shows a way of life from the past. Some fish shacks have rotted away, and others have burned, but a few exist.

Muggy and the school of fish glide beneath one. Barnacles and sea squirts grow on the pilings. Muggy hears someone playing a guitar and then footsteps. Muggy sees legs splashing into the water as a man and a boy sit on the deck. Then Muggy hears their voices.

continued

"Tell me the story, Daddy, about the fish shack."

"You've heard it before, son."

"I know. I want to hear it again." The man says, "Fishermen netted so many fish that their boat couldn't hold them all. They unloaded the fish here and kept on fishing. Another boat, called a 'run boat,' picked up the fish and took them to the fish companies in Punta Gorda."

Muggy swims near their feet. Air bubbles cling to the man's leg hairs.

The boy asks, "Why didn't the fishermen just come back and get them at the end of the day?"

Muggy circles the feet of the boy.

His father says, "If it was a good day of fishing, there would be too many. And even if it wasn't a good day, they would go bad waiting all day. You know how hot it is today? Imagine if the shack were full of dead fish."

"It would stink!" the boy says. Muggy watches the boy's toes wiggle.

"That's right. So the run boat would get the fish to the fish company while it was still fresh. That's important for any fish, but especially for mullet."

"Why?"

"No one knows why, but mullet don't keep. Mulletheads, the people who really love mullet, say you should eat them as soon as you catch them."

Muggy sees a grouper near one of the pilings. He and the other little fish hurry away.

Section 5: Gasparilla Island State Park and Cayo Costa State Park

Muggy sees the large silvery flashes of a silver king tarpon. Most fish get oxygen from the water through their gills, but tarpon also have a swim bladder that works like a lung. Like a roller coaster, they move up and down, in and out of the water. When they are out of the water, they can breathe air.

Sometimes water in Charlotte Harbor can be very low in oxygen. Schools of mullet must swim away to survive, but tarpon can stay because they breathe oxygen from the air.

A channel marker guides boats bringing people to Cayo Costa State Park. An anhinga sits on the marker and holds its wings open to dry. It watches Muggy and the school of fish twist in and out of the maze of mangrove roots.

Three brown pelicans skim low across the water. The channel is called Pelican Pass. Boats go through the pass into Pelican Bay, stopping at the docks.

Muggy hears splashing. He watches the feet of a girl and boy wading into the water. He hears the girl say, "Do you see the little fish?" She points to Muggy and the other mullet.

The boy says, "Yeah, but this is nothing like Gasparilla Island State Park where we were yesterday."

"That seemed like a desert to me — all hot sand," says the girl.

"But what about those cool iguanas!" The boy reaches into the water to pick up a shell. Muggy and the other fish dart away.

The girl says, "I didn't like the iguanas. They look scary. And they don't belong there. They chase away the animals that are supposed to live there."

"I liked chasing them." The boy tosses his shell. Muggy hears the "kerplop" when it hits the water and watches the shell sink to the bottom.

The girl says, "I liked that old lighthouse. A family lived there, and I thought about how it would feel to live there."

"Oh, who cares about some old building. Let's go," the boy says.

They turn and run back to the shore. Muggy and the mullet scoot away.

Section 6: Pine Island Sound and National Wildlife Refuge

Muggy and the school of mullet swim through Pine Island Sound. There are 17 islands in the Pine Island National Wildlife Refuge. Some of these mangrove islands are closed to the public and are home to herons, egrets and pelicans. These birds like to eat mullet, so the school stays away.

Pine Island Sound is home to many kinds of shellfish, including clams. Just west of Cork Island, the school of mullet swims over clams growing under mesh. They have been "planted" by clam farmers. The mesh protects the clams from being eaten by stingrays, sheepshead, blue crabs, tulip shells or king's crowns. The farmers have to remove sponges, sea squirts and barnacles that grow on the mesh so the clams will live.

A boat drifts above and Muggy hears the first man say, "Fishing for a living was easier before the net ban."

"You bet," the second man says.

The first man says, "Remember when we were mullet wrappers? We knew we had a school when a bunch of mullet started jumping."

"Or when the pelicans started circling and diving. Don't forget them." The second man laughs.

The first man says, "I hated it when they tried to steal the mullet as we wrapped the nets around the school."

Muggy noses the hull of the boat.

"That was the fun part. The real work was hauling that net in, pulling the mullet through the mesh and icing them down," the second man says.

"It was work, but not like farming clams," the first man says. "At least when we were out in the boat, I felt free."

"You're out in the boat now, free as can be!" the second man says.

"It's not the same," the first man says.

Muggy and the school of mullet scoot away.

Section 7: Sanibel Island and San Carlos Bay

A frigate bird soars above the J. N. "Ding" Darling National Wildlife Refuge on Sanibel Island. San Carlos Bay washes the shores of the refuge. Muggy and the school of mullet explore the shallow water where roseate spoonbills feed. Great blue herons wade in the water. Ibis sit on the prop roots of the mangroves.

Beneath another mangrove, Muggy looks up. He thinks he sees a cloud, but it's not a cloud. It's a snowy egret stabbing the water with its sharp bill. It grabs a fish near Muggy, and Muggy zips away.

The school of mullet passes the edge of Sanibel Island. A road, called a causeway, links Sanibel to the mainland. The causeway includes three bridges and two islands. The islands were made by spoil from dredging. Before it was built, the water flowed easily through San Carlos Bay. Now the islands of the causeway block the flow and push a strong current under each of the bridges.

That strong current pulls the mullet toward the channel. A loud roar scares Muggy and the other mullet. Dredges are working along the causeway. Like vacuum cleaners, they suck up the sand from the boat channel. The sand, or spoil, is pumped out. The sand is sometimes used to build the islands between the bridges.

The school of mullet tries to circle around the dredge. But one mullet is too close, and the pipe swallows it. When it is dumped out with the sand, it is already dead. Many other animals and fish are also killed. The spoil smells like rotting fish for many days.

Some of the dead fish float out into the water. A blacktip shark is eating them. The school of mullet turns away, and the shark chases them. The school zigzags in the water. Because it is so big, the shark can't turn as quickly, and Muggy and the school escape.

An osprey soars above the school and dives toward the water. It grabs a mullet and flaps its wings. It flies to its nest carrying the heavy mullet. Muggy and the other mullet zip into the seagrass. They see several manatees. The manatees graze on the seagrass, and the mullet eat the tiny plants and small animals that live on or in the seagrass. The mullet and the manatees feed together.

Section 8: Mound Key Archaeological State Park

Large seagrass meadows and many mangroves fill Estero Bay, and the school of mullet finds many places to hide. From deeper water, a seatrout charges and chases, until it catches a mullet. Muggy and the others escape.

They swim to Mound Key, a state archaeological site, where the Calusa Indians built their main village. For at least 2,000 years, the Calusa Indians lived in Charlotte Harbor. The Spaniards visited Mound Key when they explored Florida more than 500 years ago.

On this key, the Calusa made huge mounds of shells and dug canals. Muggy and the mullet explore one of the canals. Mangroves grow in it. Fiddler crabs crawl along the roots, and spiders spin webs through the branches. Muggy can hear a prairie warbler trilling its notes. Then a snook charges up the canal. The school of mullet scatter. Some wiggle between the mangrove roots.

Muggy and the other mullet turn back to the bay. They race through the canal, and the snook chases them. Muggy and two other mullet zip into the bay. A bald eagle swoops toward them and snatches one mullet in its talons. The snook grabs the other. The third is Muggy. He searches through the seagrass for the rest of the school, but he can't find them. After a while, he jumps into the air. He does not jump like a dolphin, which dives head first and curves its body. Muggy holds his body stiff. Instead of his nose, his belly hits the water first, and he looks like someone making a belly flop.

Mullet in the mangroves and in the seagrass hear Muggy jump. They glide toward the sound. Now Muggy is in a school of fish again.

Section 9: Estero Bay Preserve State Park

Muggy sees two kayaks and hears the dipping of the paddles. The paddles stop, and the kayaks drift near the mangroves. Muggy hears the girl say, "I've never seen a river like Estero."

Her uncle says, "And its been used by people for a long time."

She says, "It sure doesn't look like it."

"What did you think about that Koreshan community?" her uncle asks.

She says, "They had some funny ideas! I can't believe they planted melaleuca trees because they wanted to dry up the Everglades!"

"I know." The man drinks from a water bottle. "Melaleuca also keeps any other plants from growing, and animals and birds need those plants to live."

From underwater, Muggy watches a crab crawling on the prop roots.

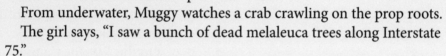

The girl says, "I saw a bunch of dead melaleuca trees along Interstate 75."

He says, "It's a lot of work to kill them. Workers have to inject them with a chemical, a little at a time, so the trees die slowly. If the tree thinks it's dying, it releases a million seeds, and each one will grow a new tree."

"What a mess!" she says. Her kayak rocks as she shifts her weight. In the shade of the kayaks, Muggy sees comb jellies and sea horses in the seagrass.

The girl says, "I'm a mess too. My arms hurt already, and we haven't gone very far on the blueway."

He says, "I love these blueway trails because it's a nature trail for canoes and kayaks. It's the best way to enjoy Estero Bay and the other estuaries."

She asks, "Didn't you say Estero Bay was the only aquatic preserve in Florida?"

He says, "It isn't the only one, but it was the first."

Muggy sees a needlefish. The school dives deeper into the mangrove roots.

The girl asks, "Can we paddle all of the blueway trails?"

Her uncle says, "We will, but not today. Let's go." Their paddles dip into the water, and Muggy shifts with the movement.

Section 10: Lovers Key State Park

Estero Boulevard bridges Big Carlos Pass and New Pass and goes through Lovers Key State Park. Muggy hears the noise of cars and trucks.

The school of mullet feeds with sea horses and pipefish in the seagrass that grows between Lovers Key and Long Key. Suddenly, Muggy sees a large shape, but he is not afraid. It is a sea turtle.

The mullet swim into the shade of an observation platform. Four legs and feet dangle in the water, two large and two small. Muggy hears the talking of the people on the platform.

"I can't believe how many turtle nests we saw on the beach," a girl says.

"Sea turtles like this beach," her mother says.

"This place is so beautiful," the girl says. "And if it hadn't been saved from development, it would look just like Fort Myers Beach," her mother explains.

"It seems built up enough, with the parking lot, roads, picnic tables, shelter and restrooms," the girl says. She moves her legs back and forth in the water, and Muggy plays in the currents that she makes.

Her mother says, "I wish it had become a park before the developer dug those canals in Black Island, where we hiked."

The girl asks, "What's wrong with canals?"

Her mother replies, "Black Island was mangrove wetlands. As workers dredged the canals, they piled the spoil beside them. It made the land higher, and now it is uplands where mangroves can't grow. That higher land is home to plants and animals that never lived there. The ones that used to live there, like the mangroves, had to find other places."

"Does that include people?" The girl rests, and Muggy circles her legs.

Her mother says, "There are artesian wells where fresh water flows from the ground without being pumped. People used to live here in fish camps."

"I wish I could have seen it before the changes!" The girl kicks both feet up. Water flies across the surface and falls like raindrops. She plunges her feet back into the water with a splash. Muggy and the mullet scatter for a moment, but they gather again. Maybe Muggy has found a home with them.

Her mother says, "The story's the same throughout the Charlotte Harbor estuary. Somehow we have to find a place for everyone — even the plants and animals — to live."

Let's Explore Further

Mullet *by Lisa Figueroa*

Mullet like warm coastal streams and rivers and brackish bays, inlets and lagoons with sand or mud bottoms. They school — swim together — for protection. Fish, turtles, water snakes and wading birds prey on them. Mullet often leap from the water. Some scientists think they are escaping predators. Others think they are clearing their gills and collecting oxygen since they live in oxygen-poor water. They eat tiny animals (zooplankton), bottom-dwelling (benthic) organisms, bits of dead plants and animals (detritus) and small animals with no bones (invertebrates). The adult striped mullet is bluish-gray or greenish on top, becoming silver with long stripes on the sides and white on the belly. Adult mullet spawn offshore in the winter, producing 1 to 7 million eggs. Many eggs are eaten before they hatch. Many hatchlings are also eaten. When young mullet reach the size of about one inch, they swim inshore to very shallow water where they find hiding places and food. After reaching two inches in length, these young mullet move into deeper water. Most mullet live 7 to 8 years, but the oldest one on record is 13 years.

Seagrass *by Barbara Davis*

Seagrasses are flowering plants that grow underwater. Like all plants, they need light, so they grow best in clear water. Most grow in the shallows; but if light can reach them, they can thrive in deeper water. There are four common seagrasses: widgeon grass, manatee grass, shoal grass and turtle grass. A rare seagrass is star grass. They all make oxygen and are food and shelter for many animals. Seagrasses also help keep the water clean by trapping soil particles with their leaves. Dredging kills seagrasses, but even a boat's propellers can cause damage. So in seagrass beds, the boat's motor should be raised or shut off.

Hypoxia *by Barbara Davis*

Plants and animals need oxygen to live. Hypoxia occurs when water does not have enough oxygen to support life. Warm water holds less oxygen than cold water. In the summer, hypoxia can happen when the creatures breathe all the oxygen in shallow, warm water. Also, warm water from the rivers flow above the harbor's cooler salt water like a blanket, causing hypoxia. This may be a natural condition, but too much fertilizer or sewage treatment plant discharge creates food for algae. When algae grows well, it blocks sunlight. Some animals can move away or protect themselves from hypoxia; but others, like plants, cannot.

Shellfish and Aquaculture *by Carol Mahler*

More than 275 kinds of shellfish live in the estuary. Shellfish feed on things floating in the water, so they work as filters. If the water is clean, the shellfish are healthy. But when red tide, bacteria or chemicals are in the water, the shellfish keep those harmful things. They can cause the shellfish to die, or the shellfish may make the people who eat them sick. Pollution has closed many parts of the estuary to shellfishing. Clam farmers lease bottomlands in some locations to raise clams for people to eat. This type of farming is called aquaculture.

Fishing *by Lisa Figueroa*

The Charlotte Harbor estuary is home for many kinds of fish. They also thrive in freshwater lakes and streams. Many tourists and residents enjoy fishing. Fish eat plants and animals, and other fish and animals eat them. They are important to the food chain, so rules are made for fishermen about the size and number of fish they can keep. Other fishermen release their catch. Although some kinds of nets have been banned, commercial fishermen work in the estuary. Fish are not as plentiful as they were in the past. Some say the reason is too much fishing. Others blame pollution or the loss of habitat.

Barrier Islands *by Carol Mahler*

Hickory Island, Lovers Key-Black Island, Estero Island, Sanibel Island, Captiva Island, North Captiva Island, Cayo Costa, Gasparilla Island, Little Gasparilla Island, Don Pedro Island and Manasota Key are all barrier islands. They are located between the estuary and the Gulf of Mexico, so they protect or shelter the estuarine waters. Gulf water washes the sloping beaches of the barrier islands. The shallow water keeps large waves from forming. With help from offshore breezes, the sloping shore also keeps sand from piling up in dunes. Although they look solid, barrier islands are unstable land masses. Waves, winds and rising sea levels change their shapes and locations in a process called littoral drift.

Intracoastal Waterway *by Lisa Figueroa*

Florida has lost about 60,000 acres, or 8 percent, of its estuaries to dredge-and-fill activities. Like digging in the sand, dredging displaces large amounts of sand to create channels for boats. Dredged in the 1960s, the Intracoastal Waterway is a channel 9 to 12 feet deep that allows boats to travel fast without going into the open water of the Gulf of Mexico. If you don't spend a lot of time boating, you may not realize that boats can hurt manatee. Manatee cannot hear low-frequency noises, such as boat motors, and they cannot move quickly out of a boat's path. Many die from propeller injuries, while others survive with huge gashes on their bodies. Pollution from boating and trash from careless people can also hurt plants and animals in the estuary.

Florida Aquatic Preserves and State Buffer Preserves
by Carol Mahler

In 1966, residents and legislators worked to mark special natural areas of fresh water, salt water and a mix of the two. The six areas around Charlotte Harbor are Lemon Bay Aquatic Preserve, Cape Haze Aquatic Preserve, Gasparilla Sound/Charlotte Harbor Aquatic Preserve, Pine Island Sound Aquatic Preserve, Matlacha Pass Aquatic Preserve and Estero Bay Aquatic Preserve. The boundaries are the high tide lines of the named bodies of water and their tributaries upstream as far as the tide reaches. Most of the open water in Charlotte Harbor estuary is included in the six preserves. Also, since the 1970s, more wetlands and uplands near the shores have been protected and are now part of the Charlotte Harbor and Estero Bay buffer preserve state parks.

Epilogue

Mullet, like Muggy, swim in schools in fresh water or salt water. They eat some of the smallest animals and plants in the estuary. Some of the largest animals, such as dolphins and alligators, eat mullet! So do herons and otters.

Near the mouth of the Caloosahatchee River, a school of mullet skims through the water. A yellow-crowned night-heron, like Nick, wades in the shallows. He would rather eat a crab, but mullet taste good too. As herons fly in and around the harbor, they see alligators and otters.

An alligator, like Missy, floats in the water near the mouth of Peace River. When a school of mullet swims by, she snaps one up. An alligator could eat a heron if it could catch one, and it will even attack an otter.

On the bank of the Myakka River are some webbed or fanned tracks and some mullet bones and scales. These are the signs that an otter, like Lu, lives here. The otter also makes "slides" where the grass is flattened down to the water, but large alligators make slides that look the same! An otter will also make a meal of heron eggs.

Many animals and plants live in Charlotte Harbor. Some, such as algae, bacteria and zooplankton, are too tiny to see. Others, such as dragonflies, tree frogs and meadow beauties, are small enough to be overlooked. Many, such as cabbage palms, mockingbirds and gray squirrels, are so common that people don't talk about them. A few, such as bald eagles or gopher tortoises, are rare.

The Charlotte Harbor National Estuary Program is a partnership. It protects the estuaries and watersheds from Venice to Bonita Springs to Winter Haven. The study area includes all or parts of Charlotte, DeSoto, Hardee, Lee, Manatee, Polk and Sarasota counties. The partners are people who live and visit the study area, the officials whom they elect, people who manage nature, people who use nature in their jobs and people who have fun in nature. These partners work together to solve problems. The loss of places where fish and wildlife live is one problem. Water quality is another. A third is how water flows through the 4,700-square-mile study area. The fourth problem is how people take care of nature.

Won't you join as a partner to help solve these problems?